Baby Raccoon

by Beth Spanjian
illustrated by Eva Cellini

CHILDRENS PRESS CHOICE
A Longmeadow title selected for educational distribution

ISBN 0-516-09063-1

Manufactured in the United States of America.

The warm summer day begins to cool off.
The sound of frogs croaking fills the evening air.
High above the ground in a hollow tree,
a family of raccoons is stirring.

Mother Raccoon climbs carefully
out of the den.
She listens, and keeps a watchful eye
out for danger.

One by one, her babies follow her
into the dark night.
But not Baby Raccoon.
He climbs onto a branch of the old tree.

Suddenly, he is scared.
Clinging to the branch, he chitters loudly.

Mother Raccoon coaxes him down.
She reassures him with soft purrs.

Baby Raccoon loves to play.
He chases his sister around the tree trunk,
while his brother tumbles
in the cool, damp leaves.

Following a narrow path to the lake,
Baby Raccoon spies a big, shiny beetle
in the moonlight.
He studies the beetle carefully!

To Baby Raccoon's surprise,
the beetle spreads its wings
and flies off into the darkness.

The raccoons follow the lake's shoreline,
leaving perfect paw prints behind them.
The family stays away from a big male
raccoon who has also come to fish.
He may harm the little ones.

Mother Raccoon finds a stream
and wades in up to her belly.
She runs her front paws through
the smooth rocks and mud.

Before long, she has caught a crayfish!
Baby Raccoon gobbles down everything
but the claws.

Back in the woods, Mother Raccoon
tries to steal some eggs from a nest.

But the eggs have already hatched
into baby birds!
The noisy Mother Bird doesn't
let her near.

The sun is beginning to peek through the trees,
and the crickets have stopped chirping.
Tired and ready to sleep the day through,
the family of raccoons heads for home.

As the morning light grows stronger, Mother Raccoon and her babies settle into their den. Snuggled together in the old hollow tree, the raccoon family will stay safe and warm until dark. Then it will be time again for them to venture out into the beautiful, moonlit summer night.

Facts About Baby Raccoon

Where Do Raccoons Live?

Raccoons live in every state of the Union, except Alaska and Hawaii. They are right at home in hardwood forests, on the prairies, in farmlands or in people's neighborhoods. Raccoons never live far from water—be it a lake, pond, stream, marsh or ocean. Raccoons are not true hibernators like bears, so they can wake up easily. Their layers of fat and thick winter coats help them stay warm and give them the energy they need to survive the winter.

What Do Raccoons Eat?

Raccoons will eat almost anything, including garbage. Some of their favorite foods are crayfish, wild grapes and acorns. Raccoons have very sensitive little paws that are perfect for picking up tiny objects. They also eat berries, nuts, grain, earthworms, snails, birds, frogs and mice. Farmers don't like it when raccoons raid their cornfields, fruit orchards or watermelon patches. Raccoons are nocturnal animals, so they usually eat at night.

How Do Raccoons Communicate?

A mother raccoon will twitter, churr or purr to reassure her babies and keep them together during their nightly feeding trips. Angry or scared raccoons often hiss, growl, bark, snort or squeal. A raccoon also uses body movements to communicate, such as baring its teeth or arching its back when angry.

How Big Are Raccoons, and How Long They Live?

Adult raccoons can weigh between ten and thirty pounds, but average about fifteen pounds. When b[ ] are born, they weigh only a couple of ounces. They fast, though, and may reach ten pounds by fall. Racc[ ] can live up to sixteen years in the wild, but few of them longer than two years.

What Is a Raccoon's Family Like?

A mother raccoon has two to six babies each She breeds in February or March, and gives birth t[ ] young ones in April or May. The babies are usually in a den, inside a hollow tree. A mother raccoon will for her babies all summer long. Some of the b[ ] young ones may strike out on their own in the fall. rest will stay with their mother through the winter leave the following spring.

What Is the Raccoon's Future?

The future looks bright for raccoons. Wi[ ] managers are either trying to increase their numbe[ ] keep them the same. Their fur is in great deman[ ] coats in the United States today. Sport hunting is popular in some areas. Though raccoons some[ ] steal crops and can be a nuisance to farmers, people want to keep the raccoons around.